GOLD EDITION

Romantic
POP PIANO

HANS-GÜNTER HEUMANN

TRAUMMELODIEN FÜR KLAVIER IN LEICHTEN ARRANGEMENTS
DREAM MELODIES FOR PIANO IN EASY ARRANGEMENTS

**BOSWORTH
EDITION**

Romantic Pop Piano - GOLD EDITION
Bosworth Edition

BoE 7100
ISBN 3-936026-82-3
ISMN M-2016-5034-0

Coverdesign: Simone Wellnitz
Notensatz: Frank Speer
Druck: Krautstein, Düsseldorf
© Copyright 2003 by Bosworth Music GmbH

INHALT/CONTENTS

YESTERDAY
(THE BEATLES)

Words & Music by John Lennon & Paul McCartney
Arr.: Hans-Günter Heumann

MOON RIVER

aus dem Film/from the Film "BREAKFAST AT TIFFANY'S"

Words by Johnny Mercer / Music by Henry Mancini
Arr.: Hans-Günter Heumann

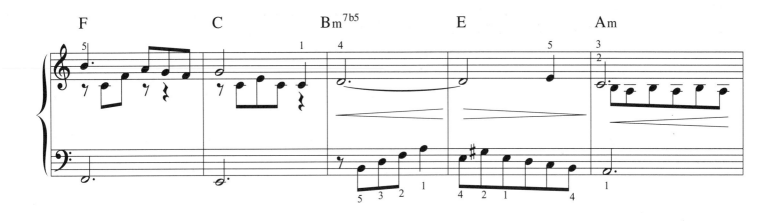

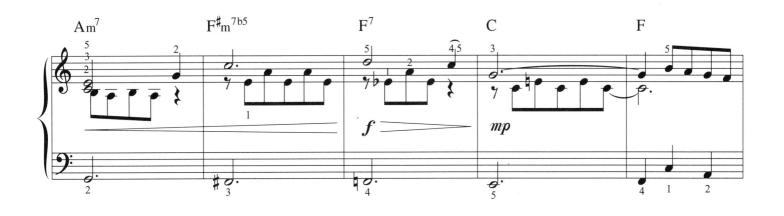

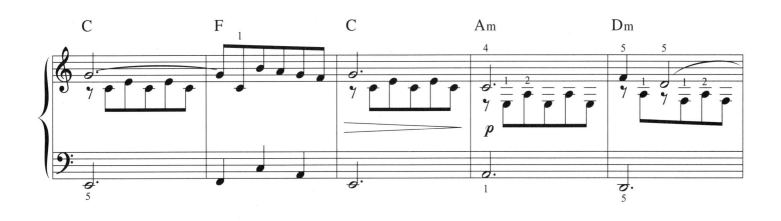

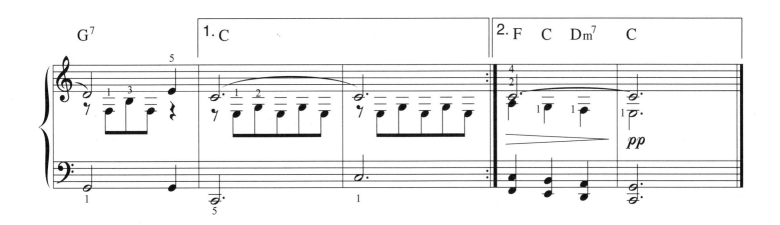

BALLADE POUR ADELINE

(RICHARD CLAYDERMAN)

Music by Paul de Senneville
Arr.: Hans-Günter Heumann

A WHITER SHADE OF PALE

(PROCOL HARUM)

Words & Music by Keith Reid & Gary Brooker
Arr.: Hans-Günter Heumann

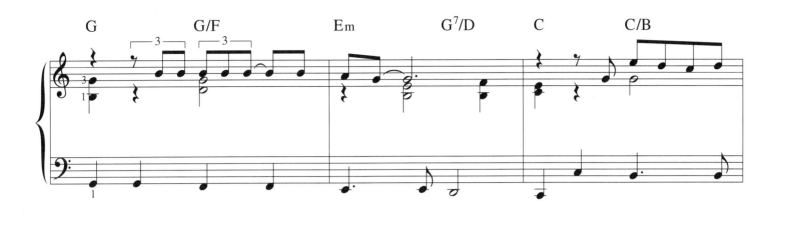

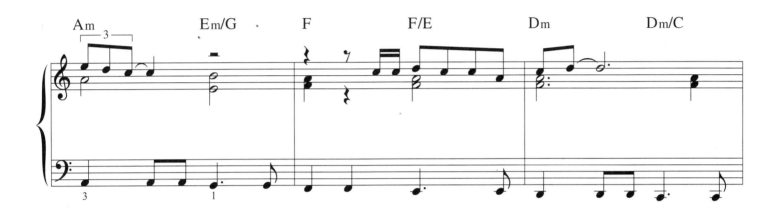

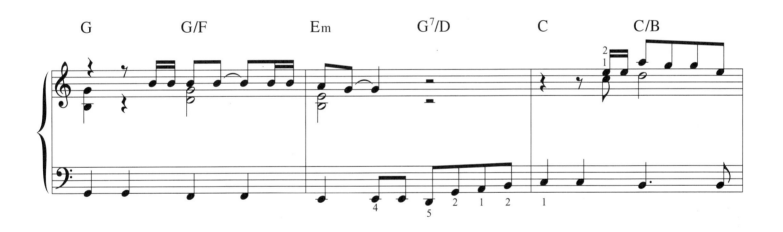

FEELINGS

(MORRIS ALBERT)

Words & Music by Morris Albert & Louis Gaste
Deutscher Text by H.-U. Esp
Arr.: Hans-Günter Heumann

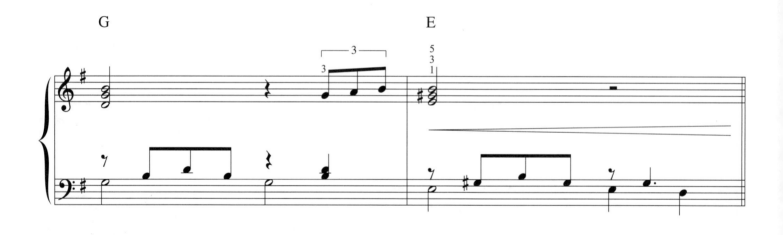

MEMORY

aus dem Musical / from the Stage Musical "CATS"

Music by Andrew Lloyd Webber
Words by Trevor Nunn / Original Lyrics by T. S. Eliot
Arr.: Hans-Günter Heumann

SPEAK SOFTLY LOVE

Love Theme aus dem Film / from the Film "THE GODFATHER"

Words & Music by Nino Rota & Larry Kusik
Arr.: Hans-Günter Heumann

MELANCHOLY OF LOVE

Music by Hans-Günter Heumann

23

MORNING HAS BROKEN

(CAT STEVENS)

Words by Eleanor Farjeon / Music by Cat Stevens
Arr.: Hans-Günter Heumann

LET IT BE
(THE BEATLES)

Words & Music by John Lennon & Paul McCartney
Arr.: Hans-Günter Heumann

LOVE THEME FROM FLASHDANCE

aus dem Film / from the Film "FLASHDANCE"

Music by Giorgio Moroder
Arr.: Hans-Günter Heumann

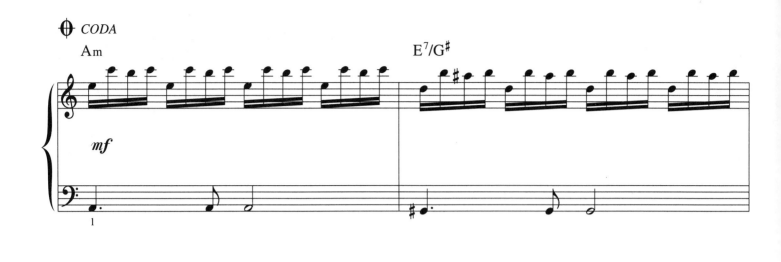

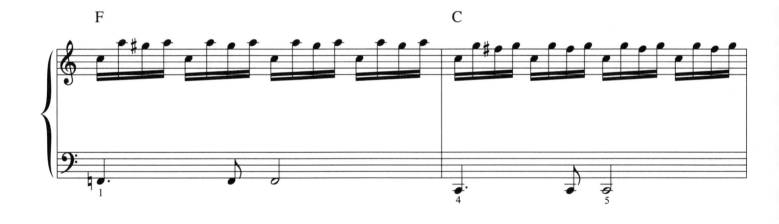

LOVE HURTS

(NAZARETH)

Words & Music by Boudleaux Bryant
Arr.: Hans-Günter Heumann

KILLING ME SOFTLY WITH HIS SONG

(ROBERTA FLACK / THE FUGEES)

Words by Norman Gimbel
Music by Charles Fox
Arr.: Hans-Günter Heumann

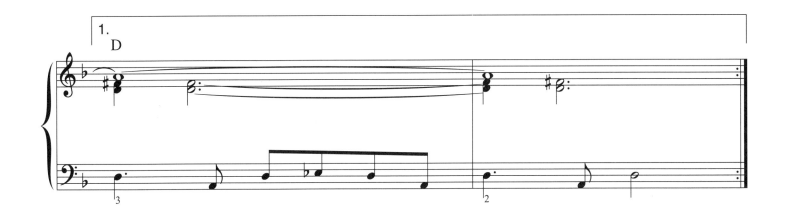

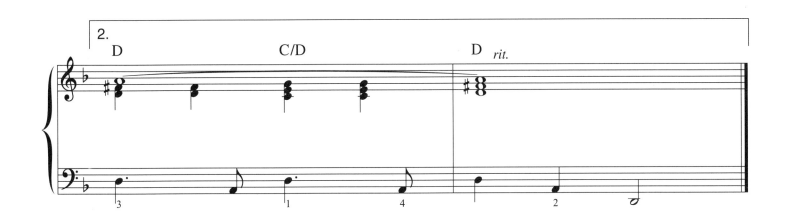

BLUE EYES
(ELTON JOHN)

Words & Music by Elton John & Gary Osbourne
Arr.: Hans-Günter Heumann

LADY IN RED
(CHRIS DE BURGH)

Words & Music by Chris de Burgh
Arr.: Hans-Günter Heumann

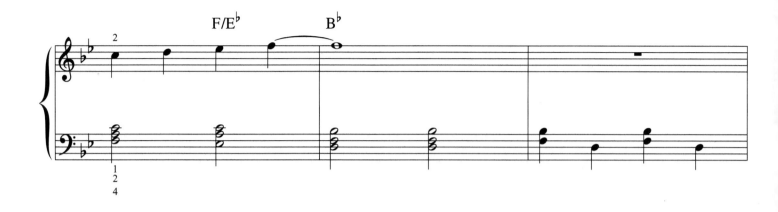

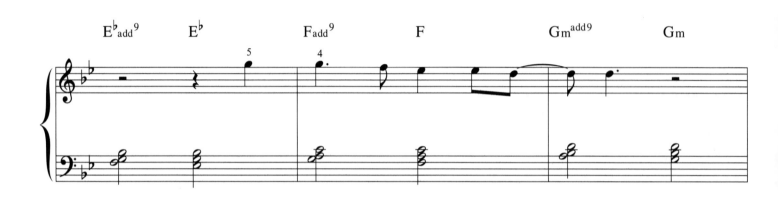

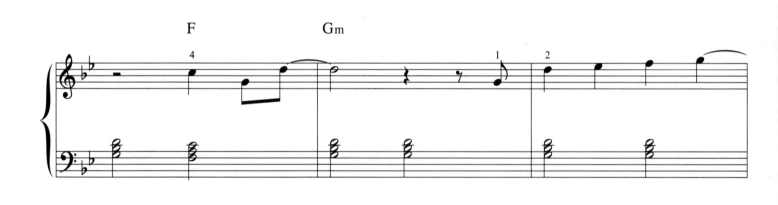

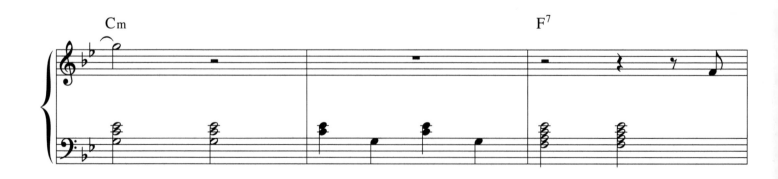

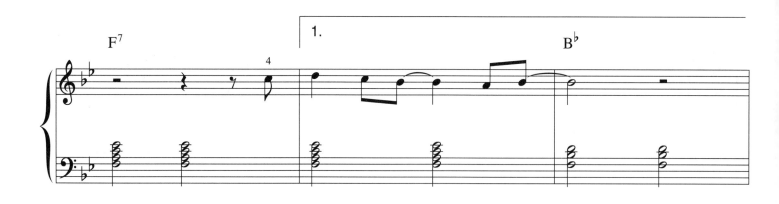

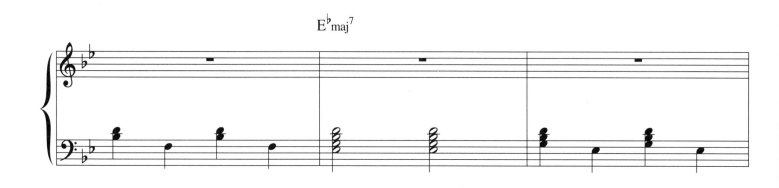

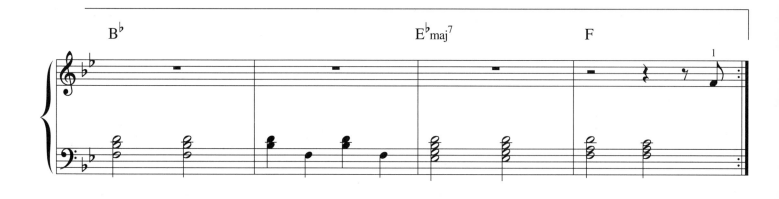

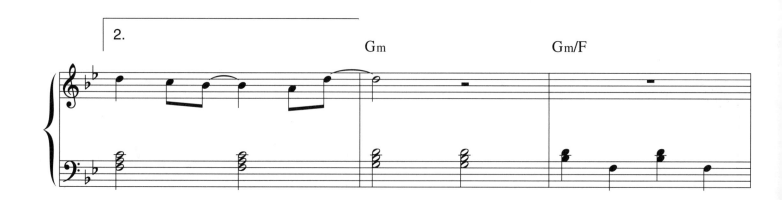

TARA'S THEME

(MY OWN TRUE LOVE)
aus dem Film / from the Film "GONE WITH THE WIND"

Words & Music by Max Steiner
Arr.: Hans-Günter Heumann

BRIDGE OVER TROUBLED WATER

(SIMON & GARFUNKEL)

Words & Music by Paul Simon
Arr.: Hans-Günter Heumann

52

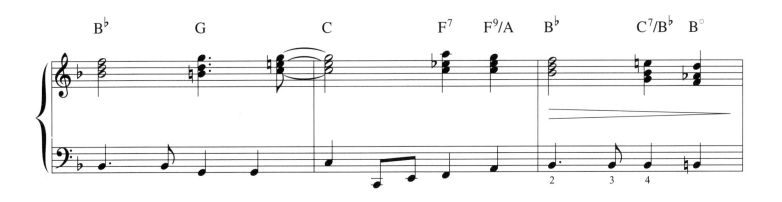

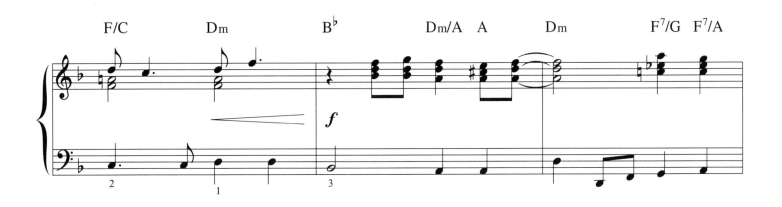

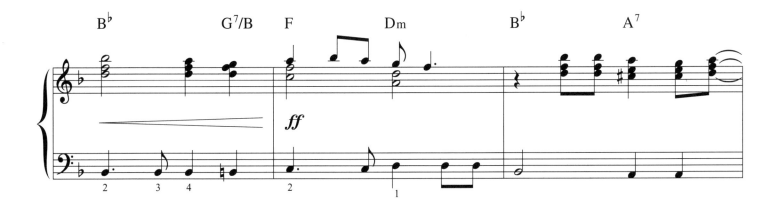

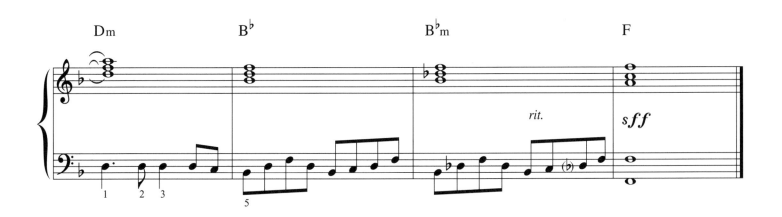

IMAGINE
(JOHN LENNON)

Words & Music by John Lennon
Arr.: Hans-Günter Heumann

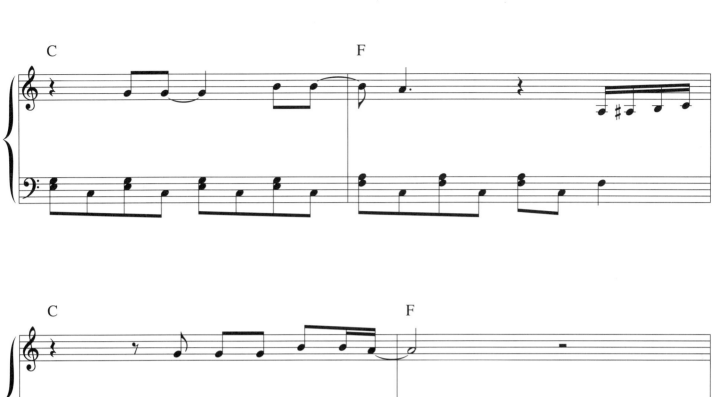

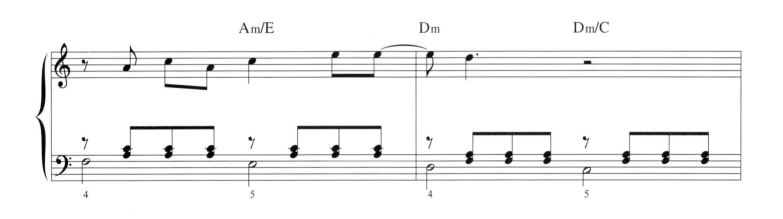

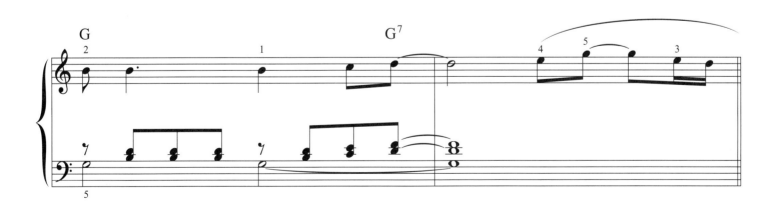

ROMANTIC POP PRÄLUDIUM
ROMANTIC POP PRELUDE

Music by Hans-Günter Heumann

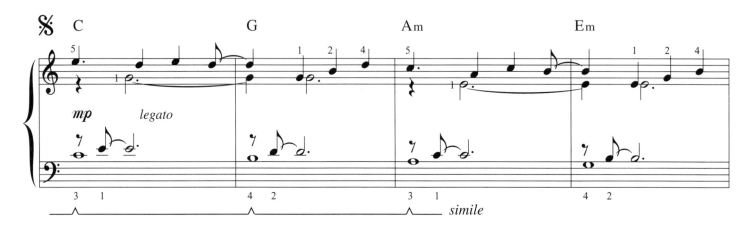

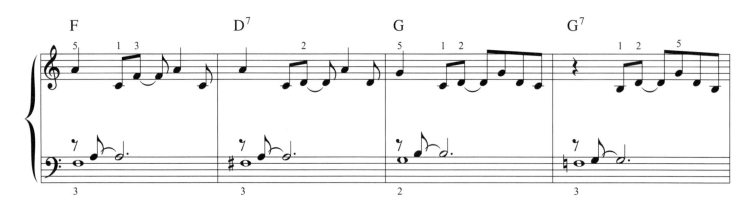

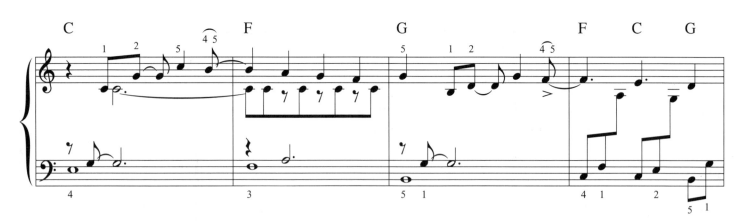

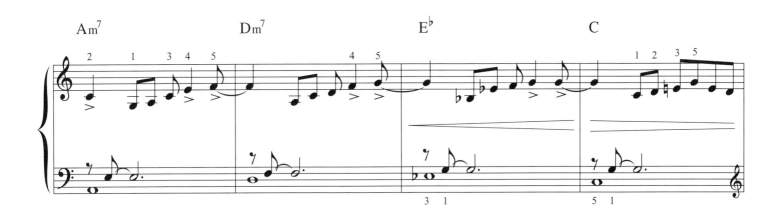

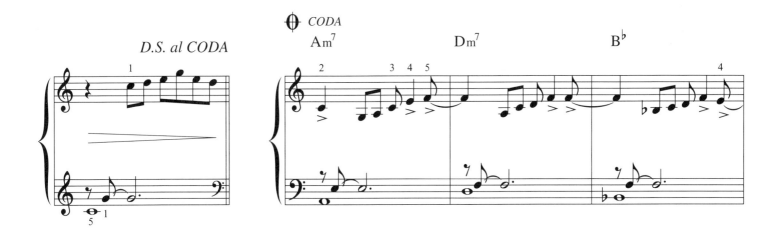

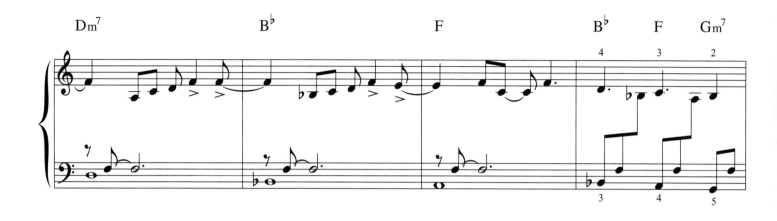

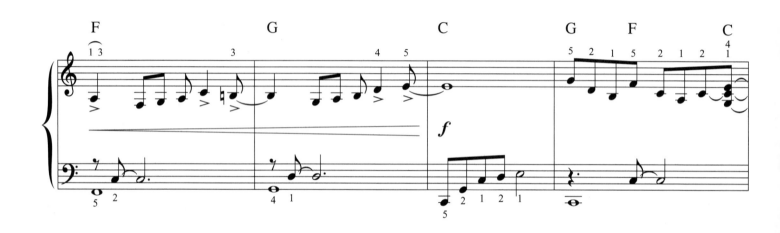

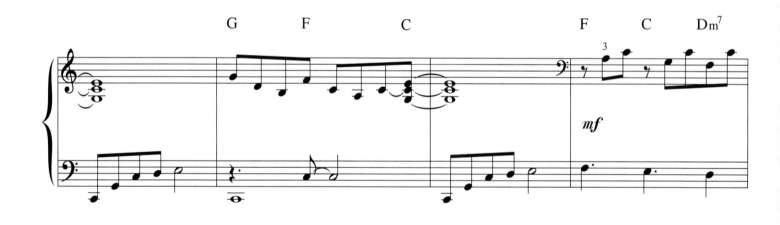

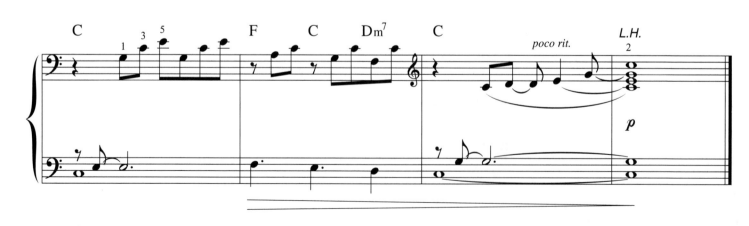

EMOTIONS IN MOTION

Music by Hans-Günter Heumann

TRUE LOVE

aus dem Film / from the Film "HIGH SOCIETY"

♩ = 104

Words & Music by Cole Porter
Arr.: Hans-Günter Heumann

WITHOUT YOU
(MARIAH CAREY / NILSSON)

Words & Music by Peter Ham & Tom Evans
Arr.: Hans-Günter Heumann

I'LL GIVE YOU MY HEART

Music by Hans-Günter Heumann

CAN'T HELP FALLING IN LOVE

(ELVIS PRESLEY)

Words & Music by George David Weiss,
Hugo Peretti & Luigi Creatore
Arr.: Hans-Günter Heumann

YOU ARE MY LOVE

Music by Hans-Günter Heumann

A TIME FOR US

Love Theme aus / from "ROMEO AND JULIET"

Words by Eddie Snyder & Larry Kusik / Music by Nino Rota
Arr.: Hans-Günter Heumann

FLY ME TO THE MOON
(IN OTHER WORDS)
(BOBBY WOMACK)

Words & Music by Bart Howard
Arr.: Hans-Günter Heumann

I CAN'T BELIEVE IT'S
REALLY LOVE

♩ = 88

Music by Hans-Günter Heumann

THE ROSE
(BETTE MIDLER)
aus dem Film / from the Film "THE ROSE"

Words & Music by
Amanda McBroom
Arr.: Hans-Günter Heumann

THE POWER OF LOVE
(JENNIFER RUSH)

Words & Music by Mary Susan Applegate,
Jennifer Rush, Candy DeRouge & Gunther Mende
Arr.: Hans-Günter Heumann

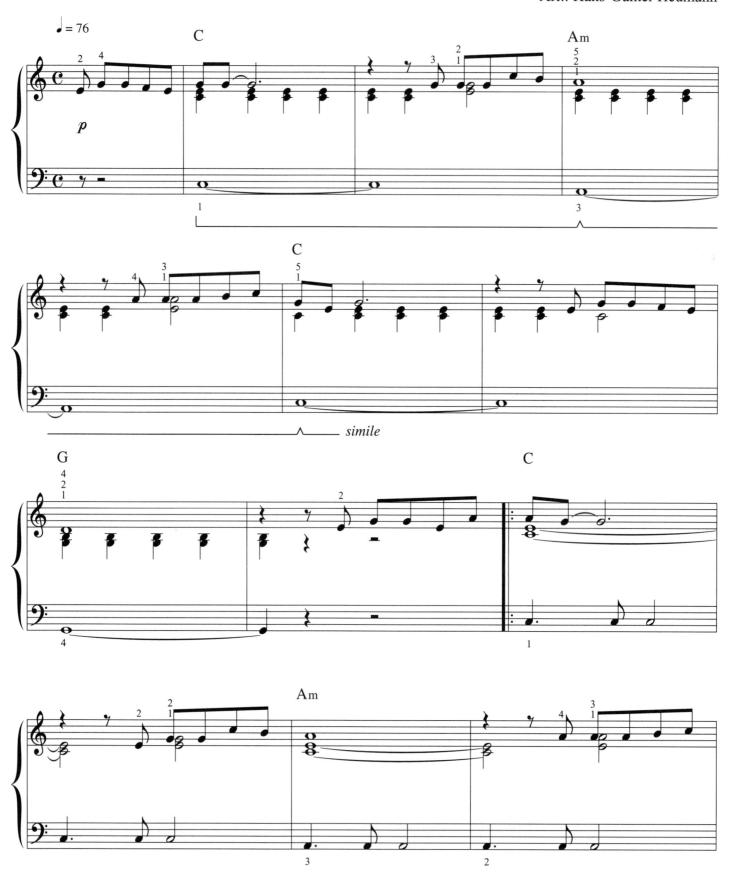

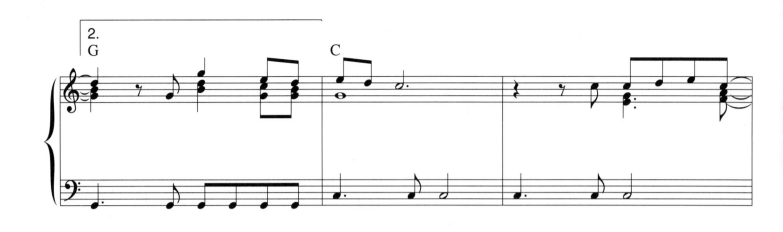

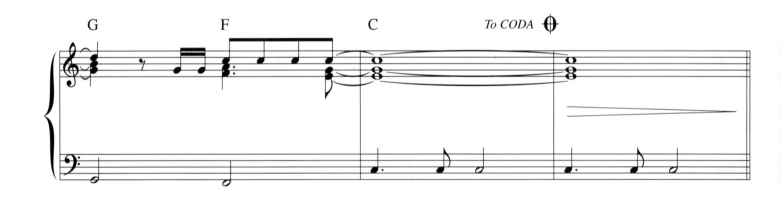

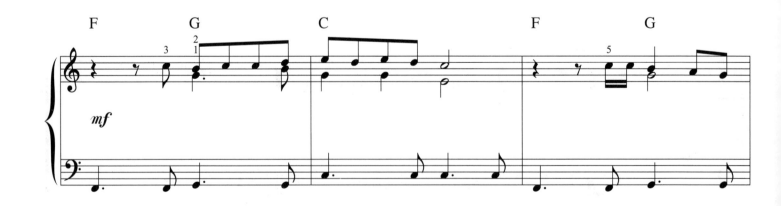

SMOKE GETS IN YOUR EYES
(THE PLATTERS)

Words by Otto Harbach
Music by Jerome Kern
Arr.: Hans-Günter Heumann

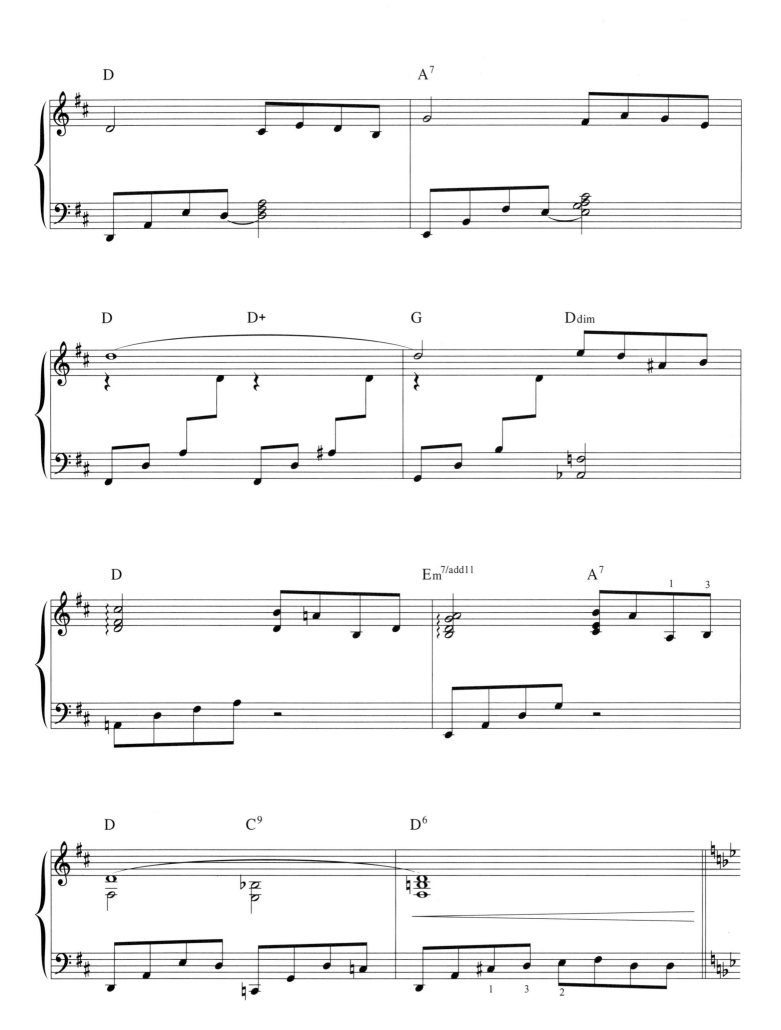

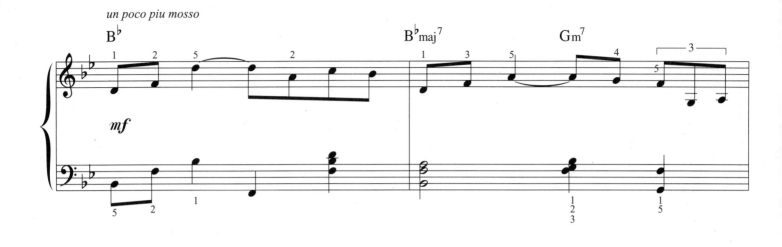

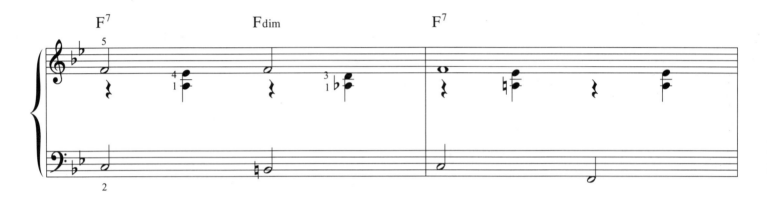

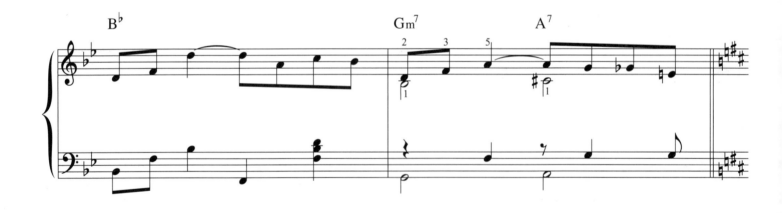

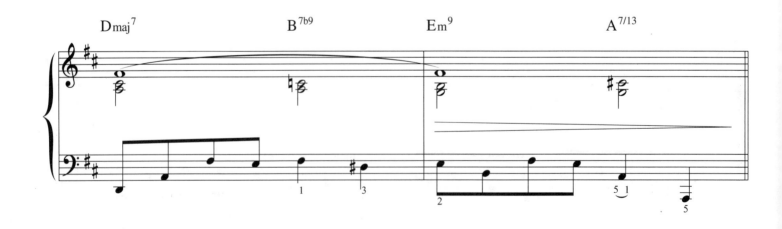